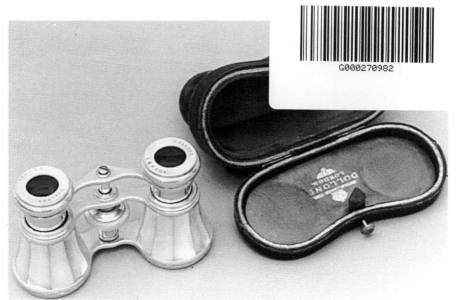

The graceful contours of this opera glass by Dollond epitomise the elegance of the classical Galilean instrument. It dates from the early twentieth century and is finished in mother-of-pearl and polished aluminium with a soft leather carrying case. The scale of all the binoculars in this book can be judged from the eyepiece separation, which is always around 64 mm (2½ inches).

BINOCULARS, OPERA GLASSES AND FIELD GLASSES

Fred Watson

Shire Publications Ltd

CONTENTS

Vision and visionaries 3
Opera and field glasses 7
The new prism glasses 13
Binoculars in peace and war 18
Modern binoculars 24
Old binoculars today 27
Glossary 30
Further reading 31
Places to visit 32

Published in 1995 by Shire Publications Ltd, Cromwell House, Church Street, Princes Risborough, Buckinghamshire HP27 9AA, UK. Copyright © 1995 by Fred Watson. First published 1995. Shire Album 317. ISBN 0 7478 0292 0. Fred Watson is hereby identified as the author of this work in accordance with Section 77 of the Copyright, Designs and Patents Act 1988.

Printed in Great Britain by CIT Printing Services, Press Buildings, Merlins Bridge, Haverfordwest, Dyfed SA61 1XF.

British Library Cataloguing in Publication Data: Watson, Fred. Binoculars, Opera Glasses and Field Glasses. – (Shire Albums; No. 317). I. Title II. Series 681.412. ISBN 0-7478-0292-0.

ACKNOWLEDGEMENTS

This book owes a great deal to the friendship of William Reid, Allen Simpson and John A. Gould, whose knowledge of the history of scientific and military instruments has been an inspiration. It is also a pleasure to acknowledge the pioneering work of Hans Seeger in this field. John Watson contributed greatly by locating several binoculars. Other help has come from Maria Baumgärtner, Helga Beez, Jacqueline Fearn, Arthur Frank, Nick Grossman, Paula Lawrence, Nick Lomb, Steve Parker, Franca Principe, Anja Schröder, Alan Watson, Archie White and Charles Wynne.

Special thanks go to Photo-Art, Newmarket, for processing, and to the long-suffering librarians of the Anglo-Australian Observatory, the Royal Observatory Edinburgh and the Royal Greenwich Observatory. I owe much the biggest debt of gratitude to my wife, Trish, for her help and support throughout.

Illustrations are acknowledged as follows: Istituto e Museo di Storia della Scienza, Florence, page 6 (top); Optisches Museum, Jena, page 14 (top); Carl Zeiss (Oberkochen) Ltd, UK, page 26 (bottom); Sotheby's, page 27. The remaining illustrations are by the author or from the author's collection. Tables 1 and 2 are adapted, with permission, from *Binoculars in the Army* by William Reid; table 3 is adapted from material supplied by the Zeiss Historica Society.

Cover: *Three late-Victorian and Edwardian binoculars. Present-day common usage tends to reserve the term 'binocular' for prismatic instruments, but it embraces all types. (Clockwise from upper left) A high-quality Galilean field glass by Heath & Company Ltd, c.1895; Aitchison's Levista 16x35 prismatic binocular of about 1910; a rather plain but dainty Galilean opera glass, c.1900, probably French.*

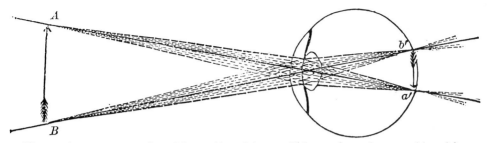

Nineteenth-century engraving of the working of the eye. Light rays leave the extremities of the object AB in all directions; only those passing through the lens of the eye are shown. They are focused to form an inverted image b'a' on the retina.

VISION AND VISIONARIES

The word 'binocular' simply means 'two-eyed'. For the vast majority of us, the ordinary, everyday faculty of binocular vision is something we take for granted. Probably most of us appreciate that our eyes work like sophisticated cameras, each having a lens at the front and, at the back, a light-sensitive retina to convert the upside-down image formed by the lens into signals that can be processed by the brain. In normal use, though, our two eyes act in combination, yielding an astonishing amount of information about our surroundings.

The key to this lies in the way the brain deals with the two images, fusing them into one and sifting through to detect differences and similarities. Binocular vision improves our perception of fine detail and our sensitivity to faint light levels and subtle contrasts. The most spectacular benefit, though, is that the two slightly different viewpoints of our eyes enable the brain to form an accurate impression of depth, so that we perceive the world in three dimensions. This remarkable faculty is known as stereoscopic vision. Although we make use of it during almost every waking moment, we are seldom conscious of it; only by covering one eye can we appreciate fully the richness of our two-eyed perception of the world.

Given all these benefits, it is not

The sensation of depth provided by our two eyes in stereoscopic vision is exceedingly strong. If it is artificially disturbed in any way, we find the resulting conflict of visual clues confusing and uncomfortable. This clinical instrument is a pseudoscope, which does exactly that. Invented by Sir Charles Wheatstone, it uses prisms to produce a reversal of depth perception known as pseudoscopic vision. Though their size remains unchanged, nearby objects seem to be more distant than their background. Window frames appear to float beyond the horizon, while faces and footballs seem to curve inwards rather than outwards. Truly, the world is turned inside out.

surprising that we should want to use both eyes when using optical instruments to magnify distant objects. The instruments we now know as binoculars consist simply of two identical telescopes fixed parallel to one another. Using them not only provides magnification but further enhances all the attributes of binocular vision.

When the very first binocular was constructed in December 1608, there was no understanding of binocular vision – not even by the inventor. He merely knew that it was more natural to use two eyes than one. Indeed, the requirement that he build a telescope for both eyes had been imposed upon him by the Assembly of the States General of the Netherlands, from whom he was seeking a patent for the telescope itself.

This man was Hans Lipperhey (died 1619), still generally accepted as the most likely originator of the telescope despite some evidence of earlier attempts. He was a spectacle-maker in the province of Middelburg in Zeeland. Probably by accident, he had discovered earlier in 1608 that a convex lens (one that is thicker in the middle than at the edge) could be combined with a concave lens (one that is thinnest in the middle) to provide a magnified image of a distant scene. These lenses formed what would today be called the objective and eyepiece of his telescope.

During 1609 news of this invention reached the great Italian mathematician and philosopher Galileo Galilei (1564-1642), who promptly set about understanding the scientific basis of the telescope and building one for himself. He eventually built several and with them made the discoveries that turned contemporary astronomy on its head. This first form of telescope, using a convex and a concave lens, is generally known as the Galilean form (although it is still occasionally referred to as the 'Dutch telescope'). Lipperhey's first telescope (and probably his binocular, too) had a magnification of about three times, while for Galileo's most sophisticated instrument it was about thirty.

Once Lipperhey had submitted his work to the States General (which did not grant him his patent), little further interest was shown in binoculars. Probably this was because of the difficulties in fabricating two identical telescopes and holding them exactly parallel with the crude manufacturing methods then in use.

By comparison, the development of the telescope *per se* proceeded apace. In 1611 the German astronomer Johann Kepler (1571-1630) published a description of a

Galilean telescope. Parallel bundles of rays are focused by the objective, then intercepted by the concave eyepiece, which makes them parallel again. Each bundle entering the eye has passed through only a small portion of the objective. Its diameter therefore limits the size of the field of view (the circular area seen by the eye). This is a drawback unique to the Galilean-type. Like all telescopes, its magnification depends on the characteristics of the objective and eyepiece, and it is adjusted for focus by altering their separation.

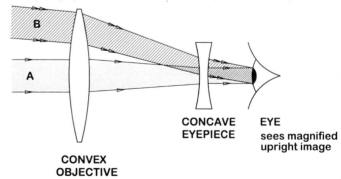

parallel rays from distant objects at centre (A) and edge (B) of field of view

B

A

CONCAVE EYEPIECE

EYE sees magnified upright image

CONVEX OBJECTIVE

parallel rays from distant objects at centre (A) and edge (B) of field of view

B

inverted image formed by objective

eye relief

B

CONVEX OBJECTIVE

CONVEX EYEPIECE

EYE (at exit pupil) sees magnified inverted image

Keplerian telescope. Here, the objective forms an inverted image, which is magnified by the convex eyepiece. Light from the full area of the objective passes through the exit pupil, coincident with the pupil of the eye as shown. 'Eye relief' is its clearance from the back of the eyepiece. Field of view depends not on the objective diameter, but on the size of the eyepiece.

telescope that differed from Galileo's in using two convex lenses. This yielded an inverted (upside-down) image – an immaterial drawback for astronomical use – but it had a much larger field of view. Kepler's design, also known as the astronomical or inverting telescope, was never used by him and was probably first constructed by his fellow countryman Christopher Scheiner (1575-1650) in about 1617. But it was a Bohemian, Anton Maria Schyrle (1597-1660), who took the additional step of inserting extra lenses to re-invert the image to its upright position and produce the terrestrial telescope.

Schyrle was one of the few early opticians known to have made binoculars. Another was the Capuchin monk Chérubin d'Orléans, who in the 1670s presented a large binocular to the Grand Duke Cosimo III de Medici. Some of these early bin-

ocular makers devised ingenious mechanisms to allow the separation between the two halves of the instrument to be adjusted to match the user's eyes. The simple hinge arrangement commonly used today seems to have been arrived at by the Venetian optician Selva in the middle of the eighteenth century.

Up to this period the images seen through telescopes and binoculars suffered from aberrations, or errors. These were not due to faulty manufacture but were an inherent property of the simple lenses then in use. The most obvious, chromatic aberration, was caused by light being broken up into its component rainbow colours by its passage through the glass. It gave rise to images fringed with spurious colours.

The great English natural philosopher Sir Isaac Newton (1643-1727) declared the problem of chromatic aberration in-

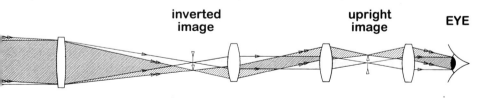

inverted image

upright image

EYE

OBJECTIVE

ERECTING LENSES

EYEPIECE

The terrestrial telescope (Schyrle's form) is simply a Keplerian telescope with additional convex lenses to render the image upright, or erect. They give the instrument its characteristic length. Together, the erecting lenses and eyepiece comprise a 'terrestrial eyepiece'.

A large Galilean binocular made by Chérubin d'Orléans and presented to the Grand Duke Cosimo III de Medici (1670-9). This beautiful instrument is probably the oldest binocular in existence today and it is preserved in the Museum of the History of Science, Florence.

soluble and turned his attention to reflecting telescopes (which use curved mirrors rather than lenses). But a few years after his death, another Englishman, Chester Moor Hall (1704-71), designed a lens with two components of different types of glass, which corrected the false colour. It was left to John Dollond (1706-61) to perfect and in 1758 to patent this achromatic (colour-free) lens, leading, after some initial controversy, to new growth in the optical-instrument trade.

Woodcut of a binocular made by D. Selva in Venice, c.1750. An adjustment for inter-pupillary distance was provided by the crude hinge at C.

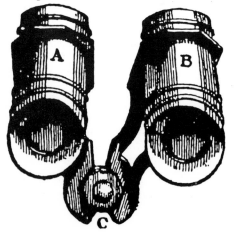

Below: Chromatic aberration. Light passing through a simple lens is dispersed into the colours of the spectrum, each of which forms an image in a different position. The result is a blurred, chromatic (coloured) image. If the lens is made of two components of different types of glass (often cemented together), it can be made achromatic, or colour-free.

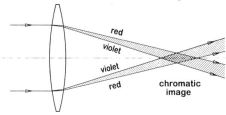

SIMPLE CONVEX LENS

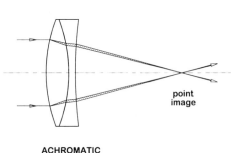

ACHROMATIC CONVEX LENS

6

A Galilean spy-glass, the forerunner of opera and field glasses. This example,with its matching case, dates from the last quarter of the nineteenth century. Inscribed 'Le Roi, Paris' around the eye-cup; length extended 11 cm (4¹/₃ inches); magnification 3.

OPERA AND FIELD GLASSES

Opera glasses are mentioned in the advertisements of London instrument makers as early as the 1730s. They were not the binocular instruments we think of today but small telescopes decorated in a manner befitting their intended purpose. In other respects they differed little from the Galilean spy-glasses made for outdoor or field use. None of these diminutive instruments magnified more than a few times, certainly less than the long terrestrial telescopes that used Schyrle's lens arrangement.

It was not until 1823 that the first completely successful binocular theatre glass was produced. At his optical works in Vienna, Johann Friedrich Voigtländer (1779-1859) began manufacturing an instrument that consisted simply of a pair of Galilean spy-glasses with their bodies joined by metal bridges. The extending eye-tubes moved independently for focusing. Finished in ivory and gilt, the instrument was designed from the outset with elegance in mind.

Two years later P. Lemière in Paris took the additional step of joining the eye-tubes as well, so that both sides could be focused together. To this was added a wheel-operated central focusing screw, resulting in an instrument that would be immediately recognisable today as an opera glass.

In the 1830s and 1840s experiments in stereoscopic vision were carried out by Sir Charles Wheatstone (1802-75) and Sir David Brewster (1781-1868). Widespread popular interest in optical instruments for use with both eyes followed, and the little Galilean opera glasses became particular favourites. By the second half of the nineteenth century they had become essential fashion accessories for theatre-goers. They ranged in style from the highly ornate to the elegantly simple, in quality from the exquisite to the decidedly inferior. Decorative coverings included coloured leathers, ivory, enamel, pewter, mother-of-pearl, silver or gold filigree, and even precious stones. The most exclusive models had eye-tubes of silver or gold; more commonly they were gilt, plated or simply japanned black. Eventually polished aluminium also became popular.

Lorgnette handles, extending in two or three sections and decorated to match the rest of the instrument, were sometimes fitted. Most glasses came in attractive cases or soft bags, while a variety of folding or collapsing instruments were made.

7

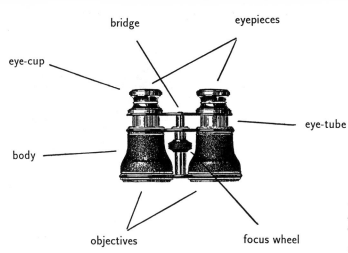

bridge

eyepieces

eye-cup

Parts of a Galilean opera glass.

eye-tube

body

objectives

focus wheel

Below: A handsome nineteenth-century opera glass in ivory with gilt fittings. Magnification is 3, enough for a closer look at the performers while still allowing most of the stage to be seen.

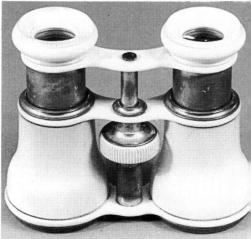

Novelties included 'jealousy glasses' that concealed a sideways-looking mirror to allow discreet observation of other members of the audience during the performance! Many opera glasses were imported from the continent, particularly France, though a few London makers such as Dollond produced instruments of high quality. Magnification was seldom more than three.

The outdoor counterparts of Galilean opera glasses also had their origins in the instruments of Voigtländer and Lemière. At first they were distinguishable only by their plainer appearance and larger size, and it is doubtful whether they were up to the rigours of outdoor use. Such binocular field glasses were in evidence during the Crimean War (1853-6); they were de-

It is not clear what kind of connoisseurs this 1st January 1903 advertisement was aimed at, for the Kalapso was positively ugly compared with conventional opera glasses. The London Stereoscopic Company marketed photographic and optical goods from the late 1850s until the 1920s.

8

large numbers. Manufacturers coined a variety of terms for their products: 'race glasses' or 'marine glasses', for example. For the most part they were referred to simply as field glasses, though it was during this period that the adjective 'binocular' began to appear on its own as a noun. Notable manufacturers included Browning, Ross and Steward in Britain; Chevalier, Lemaire and Petit in France; Busch and Voigtländer in Germany.

The best-quality glasses were sturdily made of brass or aluminium, with objectives typically 50 mm (2 inches) in diameter and a magnification of up to five. Refinements included a hinged bridge for inter-pupillary distance adjustment (to match the user's eye-separation), sling loops for the attachment of neck-straps, extending ray-shades to help keep out direct sunlight (and rain), and a hard fitted case. Official patterns used in the British Army between 1888 and 1911 (Binoculars, Mks. III, IV and V) had many of these features. More

scribed by one British officer of the time as 'useless toys'. This situation did improve, though flimsy construction and weak magnification always characterised the lower-quality models.

Like opera glasses, they underwent a golden age in the second half of the nineteenth century and were produced in very

The nineteenth-century Galilean field glass is exemplified by this instrument made by J. H. Steward of London in about 1875. It was supplied by Lennie of Edinburgh, a long-lived optical retail firm. Typical are the fixed bridge and lack of any provision for attaching a neck-strap (other than by tying it to the bridge). Diameter of objectives 45 mm (1¾ inches); magnification 3.

Triple-power Galilean glasses were popular during the 1880s. Three sets of built-in eyepieces were located in the simple eyepiece-changing mechanism seen dismantled at right. It is marked THEATRE-FIELD-MARINE, but the differences in magnification are not great. The large triple-power binocular – seen with ray-shades extended – is signed 'J. H. Steward, London', although that company did not manufacture it.

advanced was the *Fernglas 08* (1908 Binocular), a standard field-glass design used by the German army during the First World War. With aluminium alloy body castings and individual screw-focusing eyepieces, it was particularly robust. Principal manufacturers were Busch, Goerz and Zeiss.

The Galilean optical system used in all these glasses was straightforward. Each half of the instrument contained only an objective and an eyepiece, but the lenses themselves were usually made up of two or more cemented components to provide correction for chromatic and other aberrations. Thus, in a 'six-lens' glass, each objective was an achromatic doublet (i.e. of two lenses), and each eyepiece was a single lens. Improved versions with two-lens achromatic eyepieces were 'eight-lens' glasses, while some manufacturers

sought to obtain a higher degree of optical correction by producing 'twelve-lens' instruments in which all the lenses were triplets.

Although it is inscribed 'War Office Model', this glass is less sturdy than the British Army's Binocular Mk. V of 1902 on which it is based. It was manufactured in France, and instruments like this were marketed in Britain by Dollond as late as 1926. The following year, Dollond merged with Aitchison to form the optical company familiar in the high street today. Magnification 4¹/₂.

10

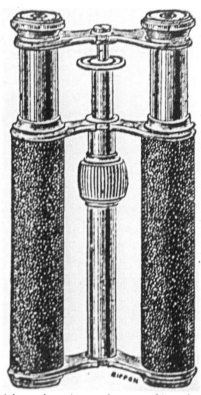

The London firm of John Browning advertised this diminutive binocular telescope in 1888. It was more powerful than a conventional Galilean glass, the long eye-tubes concealing four-lens terrestrial eyepieces rather than the Galilean's simple concave lenses. This was reflected in the price of £5. Such small binocular telescopes are also known as 'psylescopes'.

The images seen through Galilean glasses are relatively bright because of their optical simplicity. Whenever light enters or emerges from a polished glass surface, up to 5 per cent is wasted because of unwanted reflection. Each half of a Galilean binocular contains only four such surfaces (the front and back of the objective and eyepiece), so losses are fairly small.

However, Galilean instruments suffer from the 'tunnel vision' of a restricted field of view, particularly in higher magnifications. This inherent defect is not present in the Keplerian telescope, nor in Schyrle's terrestrial version of it, and by the last quarter of the nineteenth century a new binocular had appeared in which the latter principle was used.

More than half a century earlier Schyrle's telescope had been improved by Joseph Fraunhofer (1787-1826), one

A large, late nineteenth-century binocular telescope, sometimes called a deer-stalker's or (in the USA) 'long-John' binocular. This example is made mostly of aluminium and weighs only 350 grams (12 ounces) despite its relatively high magnification of 16. Made by Schlesicky Ströhlein, Frankfurt; length fully extended 29 cm (11½ inches).

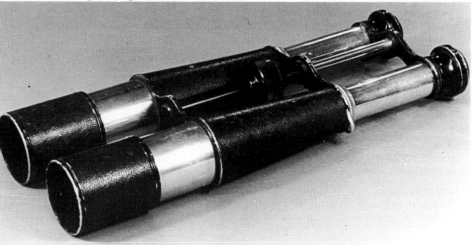

Rare nineteenth-century astronomical binocular. While it resembles an ordinary Galilean field glass, it actually consists of a pair of Keplerian telescopes and therefore has a much wider field of view. It performs well in poor light, and the inverted images are only a minor inconvenience for special purposes like astronomy. A curious side-effect is that stereoscopic vision is also inverted, so the landscape is seen pseudoscopically.

telescopes mounted side by side to produce a powerful, if rather unwieldy binocular, with a reasonable field of view. Such binocular telescopes were more expensive than Galilean glasses but were made in fairly large numbers, mostly on the continent.

Binocular telescopes survived into the twentieth century because they could be made light in weight. And Galilean binoculars are still produced today in the form of sports and opera

of the pioneering giants of optical science. He had developed a four-lens terrestrial eyepiece that is still found today, little changed, in the familiar draw-tube hand telescope. The new instrument was nothing more than a pair of these long glasses, largely because of their simplicity and cheapness. All of them, however, were rendered essentially obsolete by a new type introduced during the closing years of the nineteenth century: the revolutionary prismatic field glass.

A child's optical toy, consisting of a folding Galilean field glass with a mirror-backed compass (missing) that fitted into the centre section. Made of tinplate, it probably originated in Germany after the First World War. High-quality versions were also made, with sturdier, plated metal parts and adjustable focus.

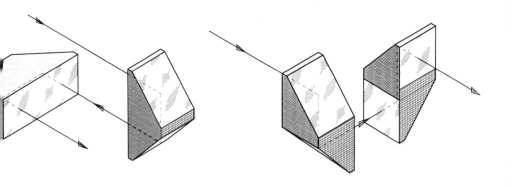

FIRST FORM   SECOND FORM

The two forms of image-erecting prisms devised by Ignazio Porro. Four internal reflections invert the image top to bottom and side to side. Placed between the objective and eyepiece of a Keplerian telescope, both will turn the image upright. The more common first form is often referred to simply as the 'Porro' type, while the second is also known as the 'Porro-Abbe', since Abbe arrived at the improved configuration shown here. Its two halves are usually placed in contact (sometimes cemented together) to form a compact unit.

THE NEW PRISM GLASSES

It is to an Italian, Ignazio Porro (1801-75), that we owe the idea of using prisms to upturn the image formed by the inverting telescope. Optical prisms are highly transparent blocks of glass with flat, polished surfaces angled to transmit or reflect light, depending on the particular geometry involved.

As an artillery officer with an interest in surveying instruments, Porro was familiar with optics and, in the early 1850s, devised two different combinations of right-angled prisms that would re-erect the inverted image. Moreover, they effectively folded up the light-path, so allowing telescopes to be made much shorter. Porro patented a terrestrial telescope that used these prisms in 1854; today we would call it a prismatic monocular.

So far as is known, Porro did not attempt to construct a binocular version of his telescope. But, beginning with A. A. Boulanger in 1859, a number of other opticians did. Their lack of success was due to the difficulty of manufacturing prisms of sufficiently high quality, and the embryonic prism binoculars were gradually forgotten.

In about 1870 Porro's prisms were independently reinvented by Ernst Abbe (1840-1905) of the University of Jena, who was also closely associated with the optical-instrument manufacturer Carl Zeiss (1816-88). Abbe was an extraordinarily gifted man, whose importance in the field of optics can hardly be overstated. He was to German science what his contemporary Johannes Brahms was to its culture: a towering figure, whose influence extended far beyond his immediate horizons.

Abbe built an experimental prismatic telescope in 1873. To overcome the difficulties with optical glass, he collaborated with the chemist Otto Schott (1851-1935) and helped found the glassmaking company that still bears Schott's name. By 1893 Abbe had perfected his idea for a prismatic binocular and, in the Schott and Zeiss works, had the means to manufacture it.

Characteristically inspired, his design built on studies of the enhancement of stereoscopic perception carried out in the 1850s by the physiologist and physicist Hermann Helmholtz (1821-94). Abbe arranged the two objectives of his binocular to have a greater separation than that of the eyes, making use of the fact that Porro's prisms introduce a step, or offset, into the axis of an optical system. The result was an enhancement of the stereoscopic effect:

13

Professor Ernst Abbe in 1893. He was not only a great scientist and technologist but also a noted social reformer. In 1889 he set up the Carl Zeiss Foundation to ensure that profits from the company went to the common good rather than a few individuals.

the landscape was thrown into striking relief, allowing the user to judge accurately the relative distances of remote objects.

It was the widened objective separation that formed the basis of the German imperial patent granted to the Zeiss company in 1894 (backdated to 9th July 1893), the prismatic binocular itself having been patented already. Production began the same year and the new instrument, with its finely engineered construction, convenience of use and pleasing stereoscopic enhancement, was an immediate success.

This first-series *Feldstecher* (field glass) was produced in three models, with magnifications of 4, 6 and 8, and objective diameters of 11, 15 and 20 mm. Seen today, they are striking not only for their diminutive size but also for their surprisingly modern appearance. Abbe had chosen the ideal shape for his glasses, one that survives little changed in many binoculars manufactured today.

Zeiss's 'new stereoscopic binocular field glass' was introduced into Britain in 1896. Prices ranged from £6 10s to £8 – comparable with the very best Galilean field glasses made by Steward, but two or three times as expensive as most. In the USA the new binoculars were made to a slightly different design by Bausch & Lomb of Rochester, New York, under a licensing agreement for optical goods that had been struck with Zeiss in 1891.

Zeiss expanded their range in 1896, introducing larger-sized binoculars and a dual-magnification model with rotating eyepiece selectors. Further changes from 1904 included bridge parts and sling loops that were integral with the body rather than separate fittings, and a slight refinement in

Zeiss produced their Feldstecher – the first successful prismatic binocular – in 1894, to Abbe's design. This is an early example of the largest (8x) of the three models available. The new instrument had to be matched more exactly to the user's eyes than the Galilean type, so individual screw-focusing eyepieces and a hinged bridge were provided. The plain hinge boss seen here was soon replaced by a scale showing inter-ocular separation in millimetres.

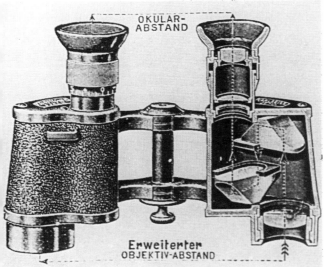

OKULAR-ABSTAND

Erweiterter
OBJEKTIV-ABSTAND

Manufacturer's sectioned view of the Zeiss Feldstecher showing how the Porro prisms are arranged to widen the objective separation. It depicts the 1904 model with improved body shell. The multi-element eyepiece is of a common type known as the achromatic Ramsden, which consists of a field lens (towards the prisms) and an achromatic eye lens close to the eye.

body shape to one that then remained essentially unchanged for more than half a century. At about this time, too, the famous Zeiss 'achromatic lens' trademark was adopted.

Other manufacturers were not slow to follow Zeiss's lead. In order to avoid patent infringement, the Porro prisms were arranged so as to offset the objectives above the line of the eyepieces rather than to each side. That way, at least, a small height advantage was obtained. Prism binoculars were marketed in Britain by Voigtländer from 1897 and C. P. Goerz of Berlin from 1899, the latter emphasising the suitability of their Trieder binoculars for astronomical observations (which gain no advantage from stereoscopic enhancement). In January 1900 the London firm of Ross introduced their new prism glasses. Within a few years most other major optical manufacturers had followed suit, usually offering a wide range of magnifications in their catalogues.

Goerz 9x Trieder of 1899 with an original instruction booklet. The arrangement of the Porro prisms is typical of binoculars made while Zeiss's patent was in force. The unusual sliding inter-ocular adjustment was replaced by a more conventional hinge in Goerz's 1904 Army binocular. That model also featured deeply recessed objectives to shade the lenses; extending ray-shades are seldom seen on prismatic glasses.

At the turn of the century the German optical industry was intoxicated with imaginative new ideas stimulated by the technological advances of Abbe and Schott. Not least among the most innovative instruments were prismatic binoculars of novel form. Such were the glasses introduced by Schütz of Kassel, which used

Below: *Two examples of Aitchison's Patent Prism Binocular. On the left is a 12x model of 1903, while the other is a slightly later 16x Levista. Superficially they resemble Boulanger's 1859 binocular, but they incorporate innovative features like a one-piece cast-aluminium body, geared swinging prism cases for inter-ocular adjustment, large-diameter objectives and, uniquely, variable iris diaphragms to reduce the incoming light under bright conditions.*

Above: *This delightful motif was used in advertisements for Busch's popularly priced Roja binocular around 1907. The 6x and 8x versions sold in Britain for £4 10s and £4 15s.*

Porro's second type of image-erecting prisms (sometimes known as Porro-Abbe prisms). They are slightly more compact than the commoner first form, but less effective at folding up the light-path and more demanding to make. Even more critical in manufacturing tolerances are so-called roof prisms, a class of image-erecting prisms that include a roof-ridge shape as one of their optical faces. Binoculars using roof prisms were introduced in 1897 by the optical firm founded by Moritz Hensoldt (1821-1903) in Wetzlar.

In 1908 Abbe's patent expired, and most manufacturers turned to 'stereo-prism' models based on the Zeiss design. Such was their success that a general uniformity of appearance emerged, characterising all but the most innovative binoculars for decades afterwards.

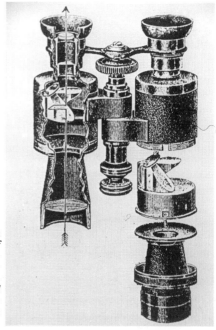

An engraving depicting the construction of an early (c.1907) prism binocular by Schütz of Kassel. It shows the light-path through the second form of Porro prisms (or Porro-Abbe prisms) favoured by this manufacturer. Provision was made for the prisms to be removed for cleaning, as shown at right. In Britain these instruments were marketed by the London Stereoscopic Company as their Prisma.

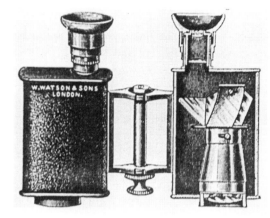

Left: *A Hensoldt roof prism is seen in this glass marketed in 1901 by the London firm of Watson (no relation to the author), but made by Hensoldt themselves. The increased objective separation did not infringe Zeiss's patent, which covered only Porro-prism binoculars.*

Lower left: *Roof prisms have one of their reflecting faces fashioned in the shape of a roof ridge instead of a flat surface. The result is a double reflection, which ensures that inverted images are turned right way round as well as right way up. They achieve the same effect as the Porro type, but in a more compact or convenient form. The diagram shows just some of the roof-prism designs that have been used in binoculars, ranging from the simple right-angled Amici prism (invented 1843) to the complex Schmidt prism (1899) found in most of today's 'in-line' binoculars. All prisms utilise the phenomenon of total internal reflection, which only works when the angle of the light-path to the surface is within a specific range. If this condition is not met, the surface must be silvered, as seen in the Schmidt and Hensoldt prisms.*

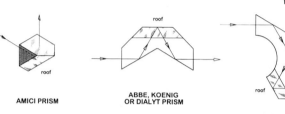

AMICI PRISM

ABBE, KOENIG
OR DIALYT PRISM

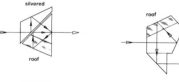

SPRENGER
OR LEMAN PRISM

45-DEGREE SCHMIDT
OR AMICI-SCHMIDT PRISM

SCHMIDT
OR PECHAN PRISM

HENSOLDT PRISM

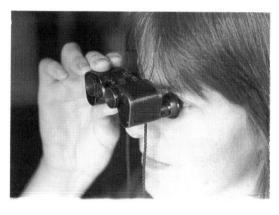

Right: *This little prismatic opera glass is the 3¹/₂x Busch Thaliar, c.1910. Similar instruments were made by Goerz, Kershaw, Oigee, Voigtländer and Zeiss, most with optional decorative finish. The Porro prisms are arranged to reduce the objective separation for compactness. A focus wheel moves the objectives rather than the eyepieces, although, as with most centre-focus prismatic binoculars, the right-hand eyepiece is also adjustable.*

Table 1. Prismatic binoculars of the British Army.

Pattern(s)	Type	Introduced	Obsolete	Notes
No. 1	8x20	1907	c.1914	Zeiss-type
No. 2, Mks. I-III	6x30	1909	1980s	Initially Zeiss and Ross
No. 3, Mks. I & II	6x20	1911	1936	Initially Zeiss and Ross
No. 4, Mk. I	6x30	1927	1936	Intended to replace No. 2
No. 5, Mks. I-V	7x50	1935	1980s	Ross pattern (Porro-Abbe)
No. 6, Mk. I	4x24	1936	1936(!)	Ross pattern (Porro-Abbe)
General purpose	7x42	1979	—	Avimo L12A1 (Ross design)

Note. During the 1960s several non-standard types were procured in quantity.

BINOCULARS IN PEACE AND WAR

When the twentieth century began, Britain was at war in southern Africa. The Boer War of 1899-1902 brought lessons for the Army in respect of its 'eyes' in the field, most notably that the official Galilean binoculars were no match for the Zeiss and Goerz prismatic glasses of the enemy. The Army's response was to introduce, in 1907, the Binocular, Prismatic, Mk. 1, based on the Zeiss *Feldstecher*. Subsequently redesignated the No. 1, it was the first of a long and varied series of Army instruments.

The No. 2 pattern and the smaller, cheaper No. 3 were supplied at first by the Zeiss and Ross companies, whose designs differed slightly. In particular, the hinged bridge components of the Ross

Below: *A unique rangefinding binocular made by Huet, Paris, in about 1905. A sliding button near the top of the right-hand eyepiece introduces a calcite window that doubles the image in that half of the binocular. This can be used to estimate the distance of an infantryman or mounted soldier by means of engraved scale plates on the body sides. Magnification 7x.*

Above: *An anonymous French glass dating from about 1910. Many of this type were taken into the First World War by soldiers of the Australian Light Horse Brigade, like this example. In pre-war days, they were sold in Britain on the civilian market by a number of firms, including Lizars of Glasgow, who marketed them as their popularly priced Nia model at 55 shillings. Founded in 1830, Lizars still have branches throughout Scotland.*

18

It was not long after the introduction of prism binoculars that some manufacturers began to produce Galilean glasses masquerading as the new type. These two examples are from Paris, c.1910. Though one of them is inscribed 'Extra Power', neither has a magnification of more than 2.

Table 2. British Army 'Special' classes, 1914-18.

S.1	High-grade prismatic binoculars
S.2	Second-grade prismatic binoculars
S.3	High-grade Galilean binoculars
S.4	Second-grade Galilean binoculars
S.5	Third-grade binoculars of either type
S.6	Binoculars of unusual design

A Paris-made 7x stereo-prism binocular produced after the expiry of Zeiss's patent. Despite its insubstantial construction, the inscriptions on it include the letters 'MG', indicating the approval of the French Ministère de la Guerre. Additional military property arrows and the 'Special' classification code, S.2, together with a registration number, reveal that it was used by the British Army during the First World War.

glasses were merely extensions to the upper and lower covers of the prism cases, a rather unsatisfactory form of construction that was common at the time. It soon gave way to the integral hinge parts pioneered by Zeiss.

Between 1900 and the outbreak of the First World War, relatively large numbers of prismatic binoculars were manufactured for the civilian market. When that terrible conflict started in 1914, it quickly became apparent to the authorities in Britain that the requirements of the Army far exceeded available quantities of the official patterns. Other sources of supply were explored (including, astonishingly, the German government) and later in the war France became an important supplier. But the home reserves in private or trade hands were vital and, throughout the war, were procured by loan, gift or purchase.

So great was the need that Galilean as well as prismatic types were accepted. Once having been deemed fit for service, these 'Binoculars, Special' were categorised and inscribed with a classification code and registration number. To these were added the arrow property mark always applied to service instruments (except the personal glasses purchased privately by many officers).

(Upper) Stereo-telescopes with extreme separation of the objectives were included in Zeiss's patent of 1894. This is a 10x Teleplast model of 1915 (an earlier Sprenger-prism instrument of the same name having been discontinued). Stereoscopic perception is increased some 65-fold over the unaided eyes, and the effect on the landscape is spectacular. (Lower) Light-path through the instrument, which uses a modification of Porro's second prism system.

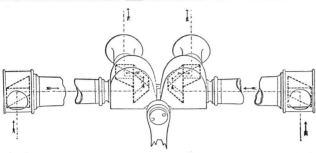

Right: *Like many stereo-tele-scopes, the Teleplast is shear-jointed so that it can also be used for observation over a wall or embankment. Though they were originally intended as much for civilian as military use, shear-jointed telescopes found real favour only for the latter and have been used in many different patterns by the world's armies. Little imagination is needed to understand why British soldiers called them 'donkey's ears'.*

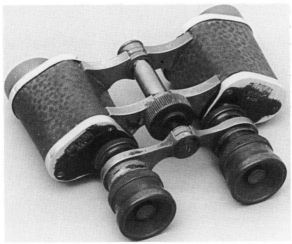

This well-used binocular, dating from the 1920s, is inscribed 'Carl Zeiss, Jena. Telonar, No. 12059; 8x30'. A double inconsistency betrays it as a fake: Telonar was Zeiss's codeword specifically for their 12x40 models while this binocular's actual specification is 6x22. Anonymous glasses engraved with Zeiss markings to increase their value seem to have been fairly common and to have originated mainly in France.

Perhaps the smallest of all prism binoculars is the Fata Morgana 3¹/₂x12 opera glass by ABC (a trade name used by August Füllgrabe of Kassel). Dating from the 1920s, it consists of little more than a hinged frame holding the optical components. The miniature eyepieces (front) focus independently.

In the meantime, Germany's instrument designers continued to make advances. In 1917, for example, Heinrich Erfle (1884-1923) of Zeiss patented the wide-field eyepiece that still bears his name, although it was not until well after the armistice of 11th November 1918 that it appeared in binoculars. The end of hostilities brought a period of great difficulty for the British optical industry, with a home market flooded with war-surplus instruments and its relatively unscathed German counterpart enjoying depreciated exchange rates. Duties eventually had to be imposed to prevent catastrophic decline.

At about this time another small but significant change occurred. The use of a 'times' symbol to denote magnification (e.g. 6x) had originated before the turn of the century, but now Zeiss began adding the objective diameter in millimetres (e.g. 8x24) to form the more complete specification used today. It highlighted the difference between ordinary binoculars and the larger 'night glasses'.

In dim illumination the pupil of the human eye grows to a maximum diameter of about 7 mm. If the disc of light formed by the eyepiece of a binocular (the exit pupil) has the same diameter, then it com-

The unmistakable outline of the British Army's 7x50 Binocular, Prismatic, No. 5. It was derived from the Ross Stepnite (introduced in 1930), which represented a significant milestone in binocular design. The shallow circular prism cases contain cemented Porro-Abbe prisms and are typical of that configuration. This is a Mk. V version of 1944; it could be filled with dry air to prevent condensation and fungus growth. Overall length 22 cm (8³/₄ inches).

A British Army No. 2 Mk. II 6x30 binocular of 1943, made by Kershaw. This example has been reconditioned and over-painted for the post-war civilian market. Almost all military binocular designs eschew centre focus wheels in favour of the more robust and dust-proof individual-focus eyepieces.

pletely fills the eye pupil and the very best use is made of the little available light. (A larger exit pupil would produce no further improvement, since the extra light could not enter the eye.) These considerations had led to the introduction of the first 7x50 binocular (by Zeiss) in 1910. Its 7.1 mm exit pupil was perfect for poor conditions, and the 7x50 specification quickly became standard for night glasses.

A significantly improved night binocular, the Ross 7x50 Stepnite, was introduced in Britain in 1930. By using Porro-Abbe prisms cemented into a single unit together with the so-called field lens of the eyepiece, its designers eliminated four light-wasting glass surfaces and improved illumination by more than 20 per cent. The premium quality of this instrument was reflected in its selling price of £21 10s.

In the mid 1930s a more far-reaching breakthrough in improving image brightness was made by scientists working independently in the USA and Germany. It is usually credited to Alexander Smakula of Zeiss, where by 1939 the technique had been developed into a commercially viable process. By depositing a finely controlled, microscopically thin layer of magnesium fluoride on to glass surfaces, unwanted reflections were dramatically reduced. Applied to binoculars, it improved illumination by up to 50 per cent. Zeiss referred to this process as 'T-coating' (for *transparenz*), but in the English-speaking world it was usually called 'blooming'. The purple or bluish hue of lenses treated in this way became increasingly familiar (particularly among American instruments) throughout the Second World War.

The Wehrmacht counterpart of the British Army's No. 2 binocular was the 6x30 Dienstglas (service glass). This example by Carl Zeiss probably predates the introduction of manufacturer codes by the German authorities. Its principal advantage over the No. 2 is an invisible one: at 370 grams (13 ounces), it weighs less than half as much. Zeiss introduced these remarkable light-alloy glasses in 1936.

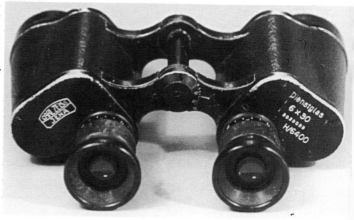

Table 3. Some German manufacturers' codes, 1939-45.

beh	Ernst Leitz, Wetzlar	**dkl**	Joseph Schneider, Kreutznach
blc	Carl Zeiss, Jena	**dzl**	Oigee, Berlin-Schöneberg
bmj	M. Hensoldt & Söhne, Wetzlar	**eaw**	R. Winkel, Göttingen
bmt	Steinheil & Söhne, Munich	**eso**	G. Rodenstock, Munich
bpd.	C. P. Goerz, Vienna	**esu**	Steinheil & Söhne, Munich
cag	D. Swarovski, Wattens	**eug**	OPW (Zeiss affiliate), Warsaw
cxn	Emil Busch, Rathenow	**jux**	Nedinsco (Zeiss affiliate), Venlo
ddx.	Voigtländer & Sohn, Brunswick	**rln**	Carl Zeiss, Jena

Note. Full stops are to prevent ambiguity when codes are read upside down.

When that war began in September 1939 the need for binoculars again became crucial. The British Army had adopted the design of the Ross Stepnite for its Binocular, No. 5, while the Royal Navy used a comparable cemented-prism instrument by the Glasgow firm of Barr & Stroud for its standard 7x50 (Admiralty Pattern 1900A). The Army's No. 2 model was made in quantity by Kershaw (Leeds), Taylor-Hobson (Leicester) and Watson (Barnet). Wray produced binoculars for the Air Ministry at their works in Bromley. As the war progressed, Canadian binoculars were procured for British service use and, again, the reservoir of instruments in private hands was tapped.

The Allies made no attempt to conceal the identity of their equipment manufacturers. However, German authorities were sensitive to information about their sources of supply, and most items of military equipment (including binoculars) were marked with a secret code indicating their origin. On both sides of the conflict, significant advances were made in binocular design. Improved robustness and resistance to moisture ingress were achieved. In the USA the Sard 6x42 set a new standard for wide-field night glasses, while both Germany and Japan introduced large, ship-mounted naval binoculars of innovative design.

The Second World War ended in Europe on 8th May 1945, and in the Far East on 15th August. The world's optical industry had undergone profound changes as a result of the hostilities, but few could have foreseen the changes yet to come.

A heavy 6x40 binocular that started its working life mounted high on one of the director control towers of a warship, where it was used to aim the rangefinder. It was manufactured by the Ealing firm of Ottway in 1940, their three-hundredth anniversary year. The large prism cases outline the shape of the 45 degree Schmidt roof prisms, and the circular knob on the base is for inter-ocular adjustment. Its thick rubber eyecups are missing.

The Wrayvu 9x40, introduced in October 1957, represented Wray's attempt to capture the popular sporting sector of the market. The Zeiss-style body pattern, with forward extension tubes carrying the objectives, characterises the older 'German' construction for larger glasses. The threaded joints into the front of the prism cases are a source of weakness since they can be misaligned by impact.

MODERN BINOCULARS

For British manufacturers, post-war prospects were nowhere near as bleak as they had been in 1919. Order books were full, the rival German optical industry lay in ruins, and it would be some years before the civilian market was saturated with war-surplus optical goods.

In Europe the partitioning of Germany also divided the Zeiss company. Jena was in the Eastern zone, and the withdrawing American forces transported 126 key Zeiss personnel to Oberkochen, near Stuttgart, where operations were restarted shortly after the end of the war. Both East and West German Zeiss companies had to overcome enormous difficulties before production could begin anew.

However, by 1954 Zeiss Oberkochen were again producing innovative binoculars of exquisite quality, though at prices to match. In 1958

The more modern appearance of this 6x30 binocular belies the fact that it is over half a century old. Made by the Universal Camera Corporation for the US Navy in 1943, it typifies the 'American' construction, in which extensions for the objectives are cast integrally with the prism cases and are less likely to be damaged. This body style has been increasingly popular since its introduction by Bausch & Lomb in 1934.

the company introduced its high-eyepoint wide-field 'B' series (for *Brillenträger*, 'spectacle-wearer'). Shortly afterwards it moved all binocular production to the Hensoldt works in Wetzlar (a Zeiss subsidiary since 1928) and in 1964 introduced an 'in-line' binocular that used Schmidt roof prisms. While outwardly similar models were already made by Leitz (their new Trinovid series) and by Hensoldt themselves (Dialyt series, since 1905), the new Zeiss was arguably the more significant development. Slim-line instruments using the same prism configuration amount to something like half

Most manufacturers included monoculars among their products. Here are two British instruments of the 1950s and 1960s, the 6x30.5 Barr & Stroud CF 20A (left) and the Wray 8x21 Panora (right). The Panora folded flat so it could be carried 'in the waistcoat pocket'; it was essentially a copy of Zeiss's long-established 8x21 Turmon.

the world's binocular production today.

Meanwhile, in Britain, binocular manufacturers were beginning to fall victim to the influx of cheap optical goods from Japan. Wray, founded in 1850, closed following a takeover in 1971. At the same time Barr & Stroud abandoned civilian binocular production, while Ross, after 145 years of independent existence, were subsumed into Avimo (of Taunton) in 1975. The familiar names were replaced by Fuji, Nikon, Yashica and Asahi Pentax, themselves long-established firms, but additionally able to market a wide range of products at affordable prices. At first quality was often poor but it steadily improved to the levels now associated with Japanese goods.

Today most of the world's binoculars are produced in the Far East. Russia, too, has a flourishing optical industry. High-quality instruments are still made in the USA by Bausch & Lomb, and in Europe by Zeiss, Leica, Swarovski and others. Zeiss is once again a single company, following the reunification of Germany in 1990. Their binoculars are now made only in Wetzlar, the East German products having been taken over by Docter Optic.

Production in Britain is limited to the low-volume output of one or two specialist manufacturers and instruments produced under defence contracts. An example of the latter is the Avimo 7x42 Binocular,

In today's terminology the Pentax 8x24 UCF of 1990 is a 'compact binocular'. Its ancestral line includes the Busch Thaliar (same prism configuration) and the Aitchison Levista (elimination of central hinge). With its rubberised protective finish, multi-coated optics and high-refraction prisms (for better illumination), it is a justly popular type.

Miniature or pocket binoculars, using 'in-line' Schmidt roof prisms, are also very popular today. This 1994 model 8x22 bears the Ross trademark, now revived for a quality range of Japanese instruments. In 1900 a Ross 8x cost £8; the £84.99 price of today's model represents much better value.

Prismatic, General Purpose, used by all three arms of Britain's defence forces. Its rounded contours are seen all too often on our television screens in the world's trouble spots.

The Avimo has fixed focus, and this feature has also been incorporated into some high-street models. A few others use autofocus technology, Minolta having pioneered commercial production in 1990. Other high-tech systems developed for military or surveillance operations include gyroscopic stabilisation to eliminate hand tremor, and infra-red image conversion for night vision. An alternative solution to the problem of stabilisation at high magnifications is the passive internal suspension system introduced by Zeiss in 1990 for their 20x60S binocular.

Large instruments, with objectives 80 or 100 mm (3-4 inches) in diameter, have become the standard binocular for amateur astronomers because they reveal fainter celestial objects. Other recent trends have a more questionable justification. Combined camera/binoculars were in vogue for a time, while the fashion for zoom binoculars shows little sign of waning. Perhaps the most significant modern development has been the introduction of multi-layer anti-reflection coatings (c.1979), now almost universal on binocular optics. They provide outstanding image brightness, even on instruments that would previously have been considered too small for serious work.

Today the industry is buoyant, producing a wide range of binocular types, many of which are very good value for money. Compared with their forebears, modern binoculars perform extremely well, while at technology's leading edge are some specialist instruments that would have astounded Schyrle, Voigtländer and Abbe.

Spanning a century of prism binocular development, the two Zeiss instruments shown here are a 6x15 Feldstecher of the original 1894 series and an 8x56B from the 1994 Night Owl range. The Night Owl uses Abbe-König roof prisms, a legacy of the Hensoldt Dialyt models.

Instrument collector par excellence, Arthur Frank began collecting old scientific instruments when he was a boy and is seen here in 1985 with some of his collection (including a group of opera glasses at upper left). Many of his instruments are now in museums.

OLD BINOCULARS TODAY

Binoculars have always been relatively expensive to buy and they tend to last for a long time. At the end of their useful lives they are seldom discarded. Rather, they are simply 'retired', so there exists today a large pool of these artefacts of the past, providing an unusual source of evidence for scientific, social and military historians. Only a small proportion of them are in museums or private collections.

Often they stay within families, and most of us have the opera glass or binocular of a late relative tucked away somewhere. Others find their way to salerooms or antique shops, while recently specialist photographic, militaria or scientific-instrument fairs have become trading places for old binoculars of all types.

Many of these instruments are perfectly serviceable, since there is little to wear out. Often external optical surfaces can be cleaned and superficial damage re-paired to reveal a binocular in admirable condition. The most common defect, however, is lack of collimation (parallelism) of the two halves. An instrument in this condition will, at best, produce eyestrain and, at worst, give double images.

In some Galilean types it can be corrected by judicious bending of the bridges, but in prismatic glasses it is a more serious problem. The method of adjustment varies from one model to another and, while experimental tinkering can sometimes correct the fault, it is best left to an optical repair specialist (assuming the binocular is felt to be worth the cost). Another option is simply to accept the instrument as a non-working example of its type. Care is needed if the internal optical surfaces of prism glasses are cleaned, since disassembly can also disturb the collimation.

Many older glasses are not marked with

27

A high-quality compact Galilean field glass by Emil Busch of Rathenow, c.1890. It has a 'quick-draw' feature that allows the eye-tubes to be extended for use simply by pulling them out, the focus remaining as previously set with the centre wheel. Other details include sling loops, extending ray-shades and ebonite eye-cups cut away for the bridge of the nose! Magnification 5.

their magnification. It can be determined by sighting a brick wall or other regular pattern through the binocular with one eye and simultaneously around it with the other. It is usually possible to count how many bricks seen with the naked eye will fit into one brick seen through the binocular; this is the magnification. Another method that applies only to prismatic types is to measure the objective and exit-pupil diameters and divide one by the other.

Often binoculars have no markings whatsoever, particularly the nineteenth-century Galilean type. Because that design evolved only slowly, they are difficult to date and identify. Prismatic glasses are generally easier. For example, Porro-prism instruments without Abbe's increased objective separation usually date from the first decade of the twentieth century (although there are many exceptions). Likewise, screwed-on (rather than cast) bridge parts and/or sling loops are associated with the same period. A curious general rule is that binoculars are nearly always older than they look!

Glasses with makers' or military marks are easier to date. The British Army's 'Special' classification mark dates an instrument before (or possibly during) the First World War. An officer's personal binocular would be marked with his name (often on the case), and helpful information about individual service careers can sometimes be obtained from regimental museums or appropriate national institutions.

A few French manufacturers, like Huet or Krauss, produced binoculars of very high quality. This anonymous 10x glass, c.1910, is also a well-made and substantial French instrument. The metal pins seen under the objectives allow it to be stood on end.

28

A neat little 8x prismatic binocular, inscribed 'Manufactured in England for E. J. Hagerbaum, Sydney'. Hagerbaum traded as an optician and spectacle-maker from 1906 to 1915; the manufacturer has not been identified. The instrument belonged to Captain W. A. Forsythe (1874-1938), who served in the Australian Imperial Force during the First World War. Similar binoculars of the period included the Zeiss Turolem and the Goerz Pagor.

It often comes as a surprise that the variety of binoculars produced over the years has been enough to make them interesting as collectables. However, there is a substantial body of amiable eccentrics for whom a binocular is as pleasing to look at as it is to look through. Many collect particular types, like opera glasses or the products of a favourite manufacturer.

While modern binoculars will usually outperform their older counterparts (in image brightness, if not always in image quality), the experience of using a good binocular is an ageless pleasure. In that regard, some of the old instruments in this book are more desirable than others, though nearly all have a charm of their own. The secret of hunting for treasures is knowing what to look for, and perhaps this book will help to achieve that goal.

An ingenious but ill-proportioned binocular oddity. It is the triple-power 6-8-10x25 made by Lemaire of Paris between the two World Wars. There are effectively three different eyepieces concealed within the oversized eye-cups, a turn of which selects the power to be used.

GLOSSARY

Astronomical telescope: see *Keplerian telescope*.

Binocular: (as an adjective) two-eyed; (as a noun) a nineteenth-century contraction of 'binocular field glass', 'binocular theatre glass', etc; hence, any kind of dual telescope for use with both eyes. In common usage the plural is often used, though this is unnecessary.

Binocular telescope: particular type consisting of two side-by-side terrestrial telescopes (Schyrle's form). Popular in the late nineteenth century.

Bridge: structure that joins the two halves of a binocular and holds them parallel.

Centre focus, individual focus: two alternative mechanisms for adjusting the eyepieces of binoculars, either together or independently.

Dioptre adjustment: modern term for the adjustment to correct for optical inequality in the two eyes, e.g. the adjustable right-hand eyepiece of a centre-focus binocular. (Dioptre is a unit of optical power.)

Dutch telescope: see *Galilean telescope*.

Exit pupil or Ramsden disc: small bright disc that can be seen standing out from each eyepiece when a binocular (other than a Galilean type) is pointed towards the light. Correct position for the eye. Its diameter is equal to that of the objective divided by the magnification.

Eyepiece or ocular: lens or lens group close to the eye whose function is to magnify the image of a distant scene formed by the objective.

Eye relief: distance of the exit pupil (the eye-point) from the rearmost surface of the eyepiece. Of particular importance to spectacle-wearers.

Field glass: hand-held binocular for outdoor use, often referred to as a 'pair of field glasses' since the original form was for one eye only. Nowadays it usually means an older instrument of the Galilean type.

Field of view: diameter of the circular area seen through an instrument. Quoted in degrees, or as a width (in metres/ yards) at a standard distance (usually 1000 metres/yards).

Galilean telescope or Dutch telescope: simple combination of convex and concave lenses that requires no additional components to make the image upright.

Graticule or reticule (in USA, reticle): glass disc in the focus of one eyepiece of a military prism binocular (usually the right-hand) engraved with a scale or cross lines.

Hunting glass (*Jagdglas*): obsolete German term for a binocular of moderate magnification.

Individual focus: see *Centre focus*.

Inter-pupillary distance, inter-ocular separation: distance between centres of the eye pupils or instrument eyepieces.

Inverting telescope: see *Keplerian telescope*.

Keplerian, astronomical or inverting telescope: simple combination of two convex lenses (or lens groups) that produces inverted images.

Magnification: number of times larger a distant object appears with a binocular or telescope than with the unaided eye.

Monocular: (as an adjective) one-eyed; (as a noun) a small telescope, usually prismatic, essentially comprising half a binocular. A contraction of 'monocular field glass'.

Night glass: binocular with large objectives; more specifically, a prismatic instrument with exit pupils about 7 mm in diameter (e.g. 7x50 type).

Objective: lens at the front of a telescope that forms images of distant objects.

Ocular: see *Eyepiece*.

Opera glass or theatre glass: small decorative binocular for use in an auditorium; often referred to as 'a pair' of opera or theatre glasses, since the original form was for one eye only. Made in both Galilean and prismatic types.

Prismatic or prism binocular: one that uses prisms to make the image upright.

Ramsden disc: see *Exit pupil*.

Reticule: see *Graticule*.

Stereo power: amount by which stereoscopic distance perception is increased by a binocular compared with the unaided eyes. Equal to the magnification multiplied by the ratio of the objective separation to the eyepiece separation.

Stereo telescope: binocular having objectives set very much further apart than the eyepieces, providing greatly enhanced stereoscopic vision. In the shear-jointed or scissors type, the objectives can also be swung upwards to allow observing over a wall or embankment, forming a 'trench binocular' or (in USA) a 'battery commander's telescope'.

Terrestrial telescope: Keplerian telescope with additional lenses (Schyrle's form) or prisms (Porro's form) to give an upright image.

Theatre glass: see *Opera glass*.

Trench binocular: see *Stereo telescope*.

Wide-field: having a large field of view.

FURTHER READING

Present-day advertising material apart, books and articles on binoculars are quite scarce. The following are some of the most likely to be found:

Beez, Helga, and Seeger, Hans. 'Fernglas-Raritäten aus dem Optischen Museum Jena' ('Binocular Rarities from the Optical Museum, Jena'), *Deutsche Optikerzeitung*, Nr 9, 10, November 1993 (in German). Some very unusual instruments.

Hanna, G. Dallas. 'The Overhaul and Adjustment of Binoculars' in *Amateur Telescope Making, Book III* (editor Albert G. Ingalls), 218-52. Scientific American, New York, 1953.

Henson, Truman. *Binoculars, Telescopes and Telescopic Sights*. Greenberg, New York, 1955. How to design and build them yourself.

Paul, Henry E. (revised by Greg Stone). *Binoculars and All-Purpose Telescopes*. Amphoto, New York, 1980. Selection and use of different types.

Reid, William. 'Binoculars in the Army' (Parts I-IV), in *Army Museum* (Yearbook of the National Army Museum, Chelsea), 1981-4. Invaluable historical account.

Rienitz, J. *Kulturgeschichte des Fernrohrs. Sammlung Rienitz* ('Historical Development of Telescopes. The Rienitz Collection'). Tübinger Kataloge, Heft 23, Universitätstadt Tübingen, 1985 (in German). Decorative and elegant opera glasses.

Seeger, Hans T. *Feldstecher: Ferngläser im Wandel der Zeit* ('Field Glass: Binoculars through the Ages'). Bresser-Optik, Borken, 1989 (in German). Essential reference work for enthusiasts.

Seeger, Hans T. '100 Years of Prismatic Binoculars', *Bulletin of the Scientific Instrument Society*, 37 (1993), 16-18.

Watson, Fred. 'A Glass for All Time', *New Scientist*, 143, 1934 (16th July 1994), 45.

Zeiss Historica Society of America (PO Box 631, Clifton, New Jersey 07012, USA). The Society's twice-yearly Journal frequently contains articles of interest.

A number of more general books contain chapters on binoculars; for example:

Bell, Louis. *The Telescope*. McGraw Hill, New York, 1922 (reprinted as a Dover paperback, 1981). Historical scholarship has moved on, but of interest for contemporary instruments.

Gleichen, Alexander (translated by H. H. Emsley and W. Swaine). *The Theory of Modern Optical Instruments*. HMSO, 1918. An early twentieth-century German optical text that was translated into English for the war effort.

König, Albert, and Köhler, Horst. *Die Fernrohre und Entfernungsmesser* ('Telescopes and Rangefinders'). Springer, Berlin, third edition 1959 (in German). Most recent edition of a comprehensive reference book.

Finally, a few works tell the stories of particular manufacturers; for example:

Auerbach, Felix (translated by R. Kanthack). *The Zeiss Works and the Carl Zeiss Foundation in Jena.* W. & G. Foyle, London, (*c*.1927).

Barty-King, Hugh. *Eyes Right – the Story of Dollond and Aitchison, Opticians, 1750-1985.* Quiller Press, London, 1986.

Moss, Michael, and Russell, Iain. *Range and Vision – The First 100 Years of Barr and Stroud.* Mainstream Publishing, Edinburgh, 1988.

PLACES TO VISIT

The following are some of the museums that have binoculars in their collections. However, only a handful have more than the occasional one on display at any given time.

UNITED KINGDOM

Museum of the History of Science, Old Ashmolean Building, Broad Street, Oxford OX1 3AZ. Telephone: 01865 277280.

National Army Museum, Royal Hospital Road, Chelsea, London SW3 4HT. Telephone: 0171-730 0717.

National Maritime Museum, Romney Road, Greenwich, London SE10 9NF. Telephone: 0181-858 4422.

Royal Museum of Scotland, Chambers Street, Edinburgh EH1 1JF. Telephone: 0131-225 7534.

Science Museum, Exhibition Road, South Kensington, London SW7 2DD. Telephone: 0171-938 8000. Binocular display.

Whipple Museum of the History of Science, Free School Lane, Cambridge CB2 3RH. Telephone: 01223 334540.

OTHER COUNTRIES

Australian War Memorial, Anzac Parade, Campbell, ACT 2601, Australia.

Deutsches Museum, Museumsinsel 1, D-8000 Munich 22, Germany.

Istituto e Museo di Storia della Scienza, Piazza dei Giudici 1, 50122 Florence, Italy.

Musée d'Histoire des Sciences, 128 rue de Lausanne, 1202 Geneva, Switzerland.

Musée National des Techniques, Conservatoire National des Arts et Métiers, 270 rue Saint-Martin, Paris 3, France.

Museum Boerhaave, 2301 EG Leiden, Netherlands.

National Museum of American History, Smithsonian Institution, Washington DC, 20560, USA.

Optisches Museum, Carl-Zeiss-Platz 12, D-07743 Jena, Germany. Binocular display.

Optisches Museum, D-73446 Oberkochen, Germany. Binocular display.